The

Workbook

CONTENTS

CONTENTS

Body + Bodily Fluids

Bondage + Sensory Deprivation

Clothes

Foot Fetish

Humiliation + Dehumanization

CONTENTS

CONTENTS

WELCOME

In the last 20 years in the kink educational field, I have discovered a few critical lessons about what folks need in order to have a healthy, creative sex life. The number one thing on that list is communication and the second is self-understanding. This book has been designed to highlight both.

I don't know about you, but those usual Yes, No, Maybe lists never gave me nearly enough room to document the nuance of my interests. So I created a place to answer all the questions that come along with an interest in sex and kink, far beyond a "yes or no, rate this one to five" system.

This book is designed to give your desires lots of room to stretch out.

I recommend setting aside some time alone and taking pen to paper to fill out these pages. Writing out your thoughts can lead to profound personal insights, and this book can be a useful tool in communicating with your current or future partners.

If you don't relate to a question or activity, re-word it or just skip the page! Feel free to use the space for your own questions and make this book your own personal erotic encyclopedia.

Princess Kali
Founder of KinkAcademy.com

HOW TO USE THIS WORKBOOK

When we're excited (the way that kink and sex makes us excited) it can be easy to forget important information that can impact the success of a scene. Relying on memory to keep track of everything is a risky gamble.

It's common to want to jump into the "good stuff" when exploring sexy play, but negotiation done right is time well-invested. These questions cover the how (protocols and health concerns), the what (activities to explore and avoid), and, most importantly, the why (what your "goal feeling" is for the scene).

It may seem extensive, but having a clear understanding of yourself will give you a higher chance of getting exactly what you desire. When you use this book with a partner, you have a higher chance of mutual satisfaction.

The first section is dedicated to helping you create your most authentic experience, including the feelings that you're seeking in your sexual encounters and intimate interactions -- this is actually the heart and center of building successful scenes and relationships.

The second section is focused on negotiation including the Top 10 Questions To Ask, Safewords, and room for both an Aftercare Plan and a Trigger Plan (and why you need one of each). The third section rounds out the first half of the book with an extensive glossary that was originally shared on KinkAcademy.com.

The second half of the book is organized around 12 categories of activities, though as you'll learn, you can change the category of an activity by shifting the energy to a different style. The most popular activities have been given a full profile page which you can personalize to reflect your desires and limits. Each category page also includes a comprehensive list of additional activity ideas and specifics. There are also 30 blank profile pages that you can label with additional activities you're drawn to.

This is in no way meant to be a complete list, but it's pretty extensive!

Feel free to get creative. Use different color pens, highlighters, anything that will make this book as personal as your desires are. If you're a switch, you can color code your writing, or use different colors for different partners.

Remember that the negotiation process is meant to be fluid and ongoing. Different activities will be appealing (or not) at a variety of levels as you progress through your explorations. You can come back to these pages to write more as you have more experiences and gain a deeper understanding of your interests and boundaries.

Let's start with the concept of Authentic Kink. This is a concept I developed many years ago that's based in shifting the usual focus in negotiation from activities to feelings.

We assume that activities will elicit the desired feeling (or headspace) but it turns out that our own personal context has a lot of influence over how we experience something. So we've been working backwards.

The activities we're drawn to are always in service of the feeling we're trying to experience, so let's figure out the feeling first, and then it's more likely that more activities can be expanded to create that feeling.

Your goal feelings are paired with your style and role to create your most authentic and satisfying sexual encounters. Understanding these elements will allow you to approach the vast selection of activities with more individualized significance.

Q: What is consent?
A: Permission for something to happen.

Q: Whose responsibility is it to gain consent?
A: Everyone's!

Q: Why is consent critical?
A: It's required as part of a healthy, happy experience. It's also the law!

Consent issues are applicable for ALL genders and orientations, tops and bottoms.

What can affect someone's ability to consent?
1.) "Newthusiasm" or overconfidence
2.) Low experience, understanding, or skill level
3.) Drugs, alcohol, medication, or exhaustion
4.) Being in "top space" or "sub space"
5.) Feeling competitive with yourself or others
6.) Relationship status or community standing

Informed consent is the most critical kind of consent. Everyone must know and understand what they're agreeing to.

Remember!
+ Consent is the responsibility of ALL parties. Give/remove your consent clearly and always ensure the consent of your partner.

+ Consent doesn't have to be sexy to be important.

+ ALL players can withdraw consent at ANY time for ANY reason. Everyone should have a safeword and safe gesture.

+ Identify and communicate YOUR wants, needs, and limits.

+ "Forced" refers to consensual non-consent. With consent originally given, the energy of the scene is that the person is "forced" so they can experience giving up responsibility for what is happening to them.

Kinksters have different ways of talking about consent and kink, using these acronyms:

SSC = Safe, Sane and Consensual -- The activities are inherently "safe," (i.e., there is no risk of significant harm).

RACK = Risk Aware Consensual Kink -- The activities are not necessarily safe - (i.e., there is a risk of significant harm), however, all players involved are aware of the risk.

PRICK = Personal Responsibility in Consensual Kink -- Kink is certainly a team sport, but each person has a responsibility to themselves and anyone else to bring their best game, which includes communicating desires, needs, and limits.

Key Concept: The one common thread that runs through each of these risk profiles: CONSENT.

How to withdraw consent

- The classic in the BDSM world is, of course, safewords. "No" is not a safeword.

- Pick something that you can REMEMBER AND SAY in alternate headspaces.

- Be VERY clear. Do not just say, "No." Say, "I do NOT consent to this," or "I don't want this; you don't have my consent.

- "For tops/dominants, good advice is, "If it's a maybe, it's a no."

- If speech is restricted, use a safe gesture.

8

Here's the thing about sex and kink. **You can be into the same exact activity for totally different reasons.** You might like to be tied up because you like the physical feeling of restraint; it feels like a hug. I might want to tie you up to restrain your movement so that I can do mean things to you -- or create the bondage hug you had in mind.

Many kinksters focus almost entirely on the action, assuming that doing an activity will create the headspace desired. But you can line up 10 people for a spanking and they can want and need and experience different things from that spanking.

This is where your goal feeling comes in: what's the feeling you're experiencing (or trying to experience) for each activity? That goal feeling can impact the tools, words, and positions you use during an activity. Different choices for each of those elements will dynamically impact how the scene or relationship plays out.

Key Concept: The way you **feel** during an encounter is more important than what you **do** during a encounter.

Discovering Your Goal Feeling

There are different ways of discovering your goal feeling, alone and with a partner. I recommend doing both if you can, but regardless, you can and should do this on your own. Figuring out your goal feelings is the personal work you can do to create the most satisfying scenes.

Alone (or with a partner): fantasy, free association, erotica, porn, masturbation.

With a partner: exploration scenes, roleplay, and wordplay.

Keep this list in mind as you fill out the profile for each activity. As you read the following list, think about how different these words feel, and how each could change a scene completely.

Your goal feeling might change depending on the activity, or the person you're playing with, or your mood that day. You might have one or two goal feelings that you use all activities to get to, or you might have a different goal feeling for each activity or group of activities.

Most people have a few goal feelings:

- **Primary** (essential to satisfying sexy play)
- **Supportive** (often related to and supportive of the primary)
- **Occasional** (needs satisfying infrequently or with specific activities)

For example, if you start with the word precious and combine it with objectified, see how that pairing is going to give you so much more specific of an energy to work from, and how that is very different if you combined, say, controlled and objectified.

But this list is just to get you started. Add other feeling words that come to mind, or look up more options in a thesaurus.

absurdity
abused
adoring
appreciated
aroused
authentic
authoritative
belonging
bratty
broken down
brutal
catharsis
challenged
cherished
clever
competitive
confident
connected
consumed
controlled
creative
curious
degraded
dehumanized
desirable
destroyed
disciplined
dominant
embarrassed
empowered
exposed
feminine
filthy
focused
free

genderless
graceful
grateful
helpful
helpless
humbled
humiliated
hyper-focused
hypnotic
idolized
in control
in service
inferior
innocent
intense
intimate
invasive
invincible
irreplaceable
irresistible
joyous
loved
masculine
masochistic
meditative
needed
nurtured
objectified
objectifier
obsequious
on display
organized
out of control
overtaken
owned

passionate
peaceful
performative
powerful
precious
predatory
prey
primal
protective
proud
regal
relaxed
respected
ruined
sacrificial
sadistic
safe
seductive
seen
shameless
skilled
slutty
special
spiritual
strong
submissive
superior
supported
threatened
tiny
tough
transcendent
transformed
trustworthy

understood
unworthy
useful
valued
villainous
voyeuristic
vulnerable
weak
wild
willing
worshiped

Add Your Own

Your goal feeling is about what's happening on the inside. Style and role are about what's happening on the outside.

As you dig into your kinky identity, or as you try on other identities for size, it's good to think of style and role as two separate aspects that intertwine to create your sexual, kinky self.

Indeed, they are separate: **style refers to the energy you bring to a scene**, to the overall vibe; your style is how you do things.

Your role is the persona you adopt -- the character you inhabit - who you are when you're doing things. Thinking of these two things separately will help you develop your most authentic sexual identity.

However, it's also important to remember that these two aspects of your identity always work together -- one necessarily informs the other.

Think of it this way: your role determines what you do, your style determines how you do it.

Let's take a pirate for example:

Role: Pirate
Style: roguish, has a lot of swagger, flirtatious

When you focus on characteristics rather than characters it will be easier for you to "become" a heightened version of yourself, or someone else altogether.

Style speaks to the energy or the vibe you bring to your play. It's the characteristics someone would use to describe you.

You might have a consistent style that's an alternate or amplification of your usual self. Or your style might change from scene to scene depending on how you're feeling that day or in response to the things that you're doing with your play partner or who you're playing with.

Style can also change throughout a scene. Perhaps you start off as a brat but over the course of the interaction become compliant.

adoring	nurturing
aggressive	parental
authoritarian	playful
bitchy	primal
boisterous	probing
bratty	protector
brutal	rebellious
bully	sadistic
calm	sarcastic
casual	seductive
compliant	sensual
creepy	sexual
diabolical	slutty
distant	sovereign
divine	spiritual
eager	spoiled
evil	strict
femme fatale	superior
high protocol	teasing
horny	tender
innocent	tormentor
mean girl	uncaring
mocking	quiet

Your role is the character or persona that you inhabit --
who you "become," what you are called. For example,
you might be a cop, a doctor, or a pirate. But it's
important to note here that you're not aiming to win an
Academy Award or even Pirate of the Year honor.

One of the biggest obstacles to role-play is that people
often feel stupid doing it, which is the first sign that
you're taking yourself way too seriously. Have fun with
the role, explore it, and commit to it for the length of the
scene.

Don't just go, "Arrgh I'm a pirate, and I want to pillage
and do pirate-y things and now...okay, can we fuck
now?" Then you look like the jackass that you feel like.
But, if you demand that your partner walk the plank and
then bind them up to be keelhauled -- now we're talking
piracy.

babysitter	king	queen
boss	librarian	secretary
concubine	master	servant
cop	mistress	slave
cowboy	mommy	slut
cuckold	nun	student
daddy	pain slut	submissive
doctor	pet	teacher
dog	pig	vampire
dominant	pirate	whore
drill sergeant	priest	witch
fuck toy	prince	wizard
governess	princess	
interrogator	prisoner	
jailer	puppy	

Negotiation is interpersonal work for a safe and satisfying scene. Communication can only ever improve your sexual and kinky interactions.

The best negotiation is a support system of communication tools, not relying on any one tool to support the whole weight of understanding between everyone who's playing.

Instead, think of it as a four-legged stool; safewords, your aftercare and trigger plans, and your most important negotiation questions to get you both on the same page for not just activities and interests, but health and safety, too.

There's no one correct way to negotiate; do what works for you.

NEGOTIATION

1. How are we negotiating?

In-person/online   Oral/written
Casual/high protocol

2. What is the goal feeling for each of us? Does that change during a scene versus after?

3. What are our soft and hard limits?

4. Is sexual contact acceptable? If yes, what kind? What are your safer-sex boundaries/needs?

5. What are the activities we'd like to explore?

6. Are there any health issues to be aware of?
- Physical health & mobility concerns
- Mental health
- Medications -- If yes, do you have it on you and is there anything I need to know?
- Is it ok to give or get marks?

7. What are our safewords?
   (verbal and nonverbal)

8. Are there any triggers we need to be aware of? (activities, feelings, words)

9. What is our trigger plan?

10. What are the aftercare needs for each person?

Bonus Questions!
- What's the last thing you thought about while masturbating?
- What's your favorite or most powerful fantasy?

TOP 10 QUESTIONS

A safeword is a verbal shortcut. The most common ones are red, yellow, and green to mean stop, slow down, and go. But we can use single words or phrases to communicate other necessary things during a scene. I've included some commonly needed ones along with room to add your own.

Check in =

Slow down =

Stop the scene =

Keep going =

More please =

Health issue =

Switch activities =

Switch roles =

Only if you want to =

I'm triggered =

I don't want to play right now =

I'm not in the right headspace =

I don't want to do that =

**Aftercare is for when things go right.
A Trigger Plan is for when things go wrong.**

In the kink world, we've long had conversations about the need for aftercare. These conversations are often gendered, or center around a submissive's or bottom's needs -- the basic concept being that during the scene the top or dominant very likely treated them in ways that aren't traditionally considered loving and caring, and so top or dominant needs to make sure they feel loved and cared for afterwards.

But **sexual exploration can be really intense** for everyone, and can bring up strong emotions for folks on any side of the equation, and anyone who's involved in the play might have the need for aftercare.

No matter what your sexual role is, you both might need a way to transition back to real life after the intensity you've been through.

Aftercare and trigger plans are two very separate needs. What you need when things went perfectly and you're feeling really positive, and good, and floaty, and satisfied? That's going to likely be different from the care you need when things didn't go exactly as planned or when there's been a mishap or miscommunication.

Think about a time when you've had a really awful day, or someone has pressed a hot button (not one of the pleasurable ones), or when you've been triggered. These can help you determine what kind of care will be most helpful if things go badly (or even just a bit sour). **Humans are complex, so when you play on the sexual and emotional edge, it's not if a trigger gets hit, it's when.**

List/describe what you need for aftercare.
(objects, emotions, logistics)

What is your most important feeling during aftercare?
(e.g., do you want to feel protected? Loved? Re-built?)

Do you need/want any kind of long-term of post session aftercare such as a day, a week, or a month later?

Does aftercare differ in a long-term relationship versus a more casual play partner?

What would happen if you didn't receive the aftercare you need?

Is there anything else that would be helpful for your partner to know for your aftercare plan?

Are there any triggers to be aware of?
(activities, feelings, words, etc.)

What does it look like when you're triggered?

TRIGGER PLAN

Are there specific actions that help when you've been triggered?

Are there specific objects that help when you've been triggered?
     (water, chocolate, food, blankets, personal item)

What kind of environment is most helpful?
   (quiet and alone, being around people, a switch to vanilla energy)

What kind of communication would be helpful?
   (no talking, talking about what happened immediately, talking about it later)

Are there any past abuse issues to be aware of?

Is there anything else that would be helpful for your partner to know for your trigger plan?

Do you feel an orgasm is an important climax to a scene?

Have you ever gone past your limits (or your partner's limits) during a scene?

What does it look like when you're having a good time in a scene?

What does it look like when you're not "into it" and/or how can you communicate that you aren't into it?

Do you ever go non-verbal or silent during play?
What does that mean?

How do you feel about crying during a scene?

How do you feel about obedience versus resistance?

What are the responsibilities of the top/dominant?

What are the responsibilities of the bottom/submissive?

24/7 - signifying a type of relationship, usually power-exchange, that is in place 24 hours a day, seven days a week.

ABDL- acronym for "Adult Baby Diaper Lovers," designating people who enjoy role-playing as infants while wearing adult diapers.

Aftercare - a catch-all term for whatever players need after a scene to recover. This is subjective, as everyone needs different things.

Ageplay - a subsection of the kink world where consenting adults enjoy role-playing various age differences.

Animal play - a subsection of the kink world where consenting adults enjoy role-playing as animals both real and fictional.

Ball gag - a type of gag where a ball-shaped object is held in the mouth by straps that go around the head.

Bastinado - a method of impact play involving striking the soles of the feet, usually using a cane.

BDSM - acronym meaning Bondage, Discipline/Dominance, Sadism/Submission, Masochism.

Big (ageplay) - a consenting adult role-playing in an ageplay scene who is considered an "older" person (usually role-playing an adult figure).

Bondage - in kink, the use of materials or physical force to restrain the movement or agency of another consenting adult.

Bottom - the person consenting to have some kink activity done to them.

Bootblack - an enthusiast for leather care, including but not limited to boots, chaps, vests, etc. This enthusiasm may be fetishized solely to the leather but can also be expressed through relationships, usually service-oriented, with individuals or communities.

Branding - a consensual permanent or semi-permanent mark made on the body through chemicals (such as liquid nitrogen) or heat (such as a cautery pen).

Brat - a player who enjoys being contrarian and mischievous in their scene. Being a brat is independent of any other role such as top/bottom or dom/sub.

Chastity - a method of kink where adults consent to having their sexual agency limited in some way. Usually this involves "chastity devices" such as cock-cages, but may also be done simply through verbal instruction.

CBB - acronym for Cock and Ball Bondage, which involves tying up these genitals for various reasons outside of sadomasochism.

CBT - acronym for Cock and Ball Torture, activities (including, but not limited to, bondage) designed to cause intense sensations to these genitals.

Collar/Collared/Collaring - the ritual action of putting something around another person's neck for the purpose of indicating a particular relationship, such as submissive. Collars are worn intentionally for whatever length of time the players consent to the relationship, and range from simply fashion to statements of lifelong commitment.

Consent - in sex and kink, the state of being willing to engage in activities with an understanding of the risks, responsibilities, and consequences involved.

Consensual non-consent - a type of play where the bottom consents to do some things they either don't want to do or pretend that they don't want to do if the top decides it. This type of play often includes "safewords" so that the players can indicate when they want to revoke consent for a particular action or the entire scene.

Corporal punishment - in kink, any type of impact play that is designed to simulate or create a consequence for an infraction. This includes spanking, caning, paddling, whipping, flogging, and more.

Compersion - a word used particularly in polyamory to denote being authentically happy about your partner's happiness in a relationship with someone else.

CRASH - an acronym for an attitude about kinky activities being "Consensually Risk-Aware Shit Happens." Often contrasted with RACK, PRICK, and SSC.

Cross-dressing - the kink of wearing clothes of some other gender than the one you usually present.

Cruise (flirting) - from the leather community, "cruising" is actively looking to find a partner for some activity (often at parties, bars, or other events).

Cuckold/ing - the particular kink of one person knowing about or watching their partner have sex with another person, often role-played as being against the will of the one watching (the cuckold).

DDlg - acronym indicating a "Daddy Dom, Little Girl" relationship in which consenting adults choose to take on the specific roles. Often characterized by the "Daddy" providing material and/or emotional care and support for the "Girl," who is usually the submissive partner in the relationship.

DM - acronym for Dungeon Monitor, a person designated within an event space to help create a safe and supportive environment for the people playing there, often through observance of the space rules as well as experience in helping with potential issues during play if asked

.**Dom/Dominant/Domme** - the person in a power exchange relationship who decides what will happen.

Dollification - a kink where clothing, makeup, accessories, and mental stimulation is used to allow a consenting adult to role-play their idea of a "doll" (sometimes active, sometimes passive).

Drop - the state after a scene, play party, or convention where the body has been depleted of things like water, endorphins, adrenaline, serotonin, or simply rest. Often characterized by fatigue, depression, self-doubt, and other negative emotions. "Drop" is countered by aftercare, whether personal or from a partner. AKA "sub drop" "top drop" or "con drop."

D/s - acronym for dominance and submission.

Dungeon - in kink, an area designated for BDSM play, often equipped with furniture designed to facilitate impact play, bondage, and other activities.

Edgeplay - a subjective term used by kinksters to talk about play that has a higher risk profile than their usual play. This can be physically, mentally, or both, and usually involves further discussion on how to mitigate the risks and handle the potential outcomes of this kind of play.

Edging - often used as part of chastity play, this refers to when someone is brought very close to having an orgasm without actually having one, either through masturbation or outside stimulation.

Electro play - any kind of play that involves the use of electrodes for direct stimulation of the body.Fetish - the technical meaning of this is any non-sexual thing that a person requires in order to achieve sexual climax. In common parlance, it simply means something that brings a particular form of enjoyment, whether sexual or not.

FemDom/FemmeDomme - a femme-presenting dominant person.

Figging - using raw ginger root, usually carved into an insertable shape, to stimulate the genitals (usually the anus and rectum, but also used for urethras, clitoral hoods, and vulvas/vaginas).

Fire play - any kind of kinky activity involving the proximity or direct application of flames to the body. Responsible fire play requires in-person training and uses many safety precautions and specific forms of flame and instruments to ensure that no one gets permanently injured, but this is generally considered one of the more dangerous forms of play.

Fisting - the act of inserting an entire hand into a vagina or rectum for sexual pleasure.

Flogger - an impact play implement usually consisting of a handle with several flexible "falls" (made of various materials, but usually leather) attached. The handle is swung by the top so that the falls hit with some degree of force on the bottom's body to produce a wide range of sensations.

Florentine - a particular style of impact play involving two implements swung in a figure-eight pattern to produce rapid strikes on the body.

Furry - a person who enjoys role-playing (sexually or otherwise) anthropomorphized animals as part of their play. Their "fursona" may be entirely virtual (such as online) or involve various costumes or props (such as kitten ears or even full-body suits).

Gender Fluid - describing a person who may move between more than one gender (not limited to male or female).

Genderqueer - any gender that is different than the socially constructed "norms" associated with a person's biological sex.

Genitorture - the act of intensely stimulating the genitals using various implements or forms of play that could be described as "painful."

Golden Showers - the act of one adult deliberately peeing on another consenting adult.

Gorean - a form of power exchange based loosely on the fantasy world created by John Norman in the series of "Gor" books.

Hanky Code - An evolving method coming from the gay leather scene of signifying your role and interest in particular kinky activities through the color and position of a bandanna.

Hard limit - any part of kink that a person refuses to engage in, usually set as a boundary when collaborating to plan a scene.

Hedonist - a person who seeks fulfillment through pleasure; in kink, often denoting a person who is more interested in sensations and experiences than relationships.

Hogtie - any form of bondage that includes tying both wrists to the ankles, usually behind a person's back when they are laying facedown.

Impact play - any form of kinky activity that involves the body being struck with some degree of force, either with another part of the body (such as spanking or kicking) or with an implement (such as a flogger or paddle).

Kajira/Kajirus - a submissive person in a Gorean style of play.

Kink-friendly - someone who does not consider themselves kinky but supports those who do.

Kinbaku - a Japanese term that translates as "tying tightly" and is used in the west to describe a style of tying that is considered by some to be more complex on physical, emotional, and mental levels than other forms of rope bondage.

Leatherman/Leatherwoman - a person who identifies with some form of Leather culture.

Leather House/ Leather Family - a group of people who identify their relationships and connections as some form of Leather culture.

Little - an adult who enjoys taking on childlike characteristics.

Masochism/Masochist - named after the author Sader-Masoch, this is the general characteristic or identity of taking pleasure through enduring some form of suffering.

Master/slave - a particular form of consensual power exchange relationship based loosely on some form of cultural slavery.

Mindfuck - any form of play that involves a person doubting their own perception of reality.

Mummification - the act of wrapping a person's entire body with some restraining material, often Saran Wrap, bondage tape, or with specially-designed latex or leather suits.

Munch - an informal gathering of kinky people, often at a cafe, restaurant, or bar, for the purpose of socializing rather than cruising or play.

Negotiation - a term used to describe the conversation before play where two partners collaborate to create a scene that will be as satisfying as possible to both without crossing any hard limits.

Newbie - a term for someone who is inexperienced in a particular form of kink. It is entirely possible to be expert at one kind of kink and still be a "newbie" to some other kind.

New Guard - often used in the Leather community to denote someone who does not identify completely with "Old Guard" traditions or values.

Old Guard - often used in the Leather community to denote someone who identifies with the values they consider to be from the original founders of the Leather community.

OTK - acronym for "over-the-knee," a form of spanking impact play where the bottom is bent over the lap of the top.

Pegging - a form of strap-on play usually involving a man being fucked anally using a dildo with a harness.

Play party - a gathering where kinky and social activities are encouraged, often taking place at a dungeon with dungeon monitors (DMs).

Polyamory - a relationship style involving multiple romantic relationships with the full knowledge and support of everyone involved.

PRICK - an acronym for an attitude about kinky activities being "Personally Responsible Informed Consensual Kink." Often contrasted with RACK, CRASH, and SSC.

Primal - a style of play that eschews intellectual and complex roles in favor of instinctual and animalistic behaviors and appetites, still within a consensual and risk-aware collaboration.

ProDomme/Professional Dominatrix - a woman with the skills, experience, and resources to provide dominant BDSM activities to paying clients.

Protocol - a formalized way of doing things, often used to describe rituals or expectations in a power exchange relationship such as kneeling, verbal honorifics, etc.

RACK - an acronym for an attitude about kinky activities being "Risk Aware Consensual Kink." Often contrasted with SSC, PRICK, or CRASH.

Roleplay - Roleplay can be a fantasy role that you playfully take on for a short period of time, or it can refer to a role that you take more seriously and forms a central part of your kink identity.

Sadism/Sadist - within kink terminology, this is a person who takes pleasure in the consensual suffering of others.

SAM - Smart Ass Masochist - this is a type of "brat" who often will mock the person topping them, usually in an effort to get the person to top them more intensely.

SSC - an acronym for an attitude about kinky activities being Safe, Sane, and Consensual, attributed to slave david stein. Often contrasted with RACK, CRASH, and PRICK.

Safeword - a word designated in the initial planning of a scene that would mean that everything needed to stop while the players check in with each other. This is usually something that would not normally be said ("Rutabaga!") and can be used by anyone in the scene.

Scene - a period of time agreed upon by kinky people during which they will consent to some kind of play.

Service submissive - a person who gets satisfaction out of doing things for other people, either individually or as a community. These can range from personal attendants to sexual acts to positions of leadership.

Sissy - a man who has been feminized, often under the direction of a dominant, through clothing, makeup, body language, sexual activities, or simple words, or any combination thereof.

Slave - a person who has consented to an extreme method of power exchange resembling some form of historical slavery, but within a modern, mutually-satisfying context.

Soft limit - a phrase to signify a kinky activity that a person usually does not want to engage in but which they may decide to explore under the right circumstances. Soft limits are still limits, and require discussion before they can be changed.

Submissive -a person who tries to do what the Dominant has decided they should do.

Sub drop/Top drop - the state after a scene where the body has been depleted of things like water, endorphins, adrenaline, serotonin, or simply rest. Often characterized by fatigue, depression, self-doubt, and other negative emotions. "Drop" is countered by aftercare, whether personal or from a partner.

Sub space/Top space - a state of "flow" where a person feels they are completely embodying their presence as a top, bottom, submissive, or dominant.

Switch - a person who enjoys more than one state of top, bottom, dominant, or submissive. They do not have to be one or the other at any given time, and can be any combination simultaneously.

Swinging - a form of socializing focused on sex with multiple partners.

Tease and denial - often associated with "edging" and "chastity play," this kind of kink involves stimulating a partner sexually (through actions or words) and denying them release or satisfaction.

TNG - acronym for "The Next Generation," an unofficial group within kink communities usually designed to benefit only kinksters under a certain age (usually 35).

Top - the person actively doing some kink activity to the bottom.

Topping from the bottom - a phrase meant to indicate that a bottom is directing the top in how they want to be treated within a scene. Originally derogatory, it is now widely understood to be simply a means of communicating desires and limits and therefore a very useful thing to do.

TPE - an acronym for "Total Power Exchange," a form of relationship where one partner agrees to let the other have as much control as possible over their behavior, often extending into everyday life, finances, and biological functions such as eating and going to the bathroom.

Vanilla - a term meant to denote a socialized "norm" of sexual behavior.

Warm up - the equivalent of foreplay in a kink scene, this is the slow and incremental increase of sensation or impact to allow the bottom to acclimate to the scene and hopefully play longer.

WIITWD - acronym for "What It Is That We Do," meant to indicate the wide spectrum of kink activities as opposed to "vanilla" behavior.

ACTIVITY PROFILES

There are (at least) two ways to use these Activity Profile's.

OPTION 1:

I recommend that you focus on picking your top 5 or 10 interests to start with rather than trying to figure out ALL THE THINGS that you want to do. After picking your top activities, you can go through the negotiation questions specifically for each activity, including any previous experience you've had and any details about your interest and limits (for example; I really enjoy/desire bondage but need to have my hands free).

OPTION 2:

The more traditional way of using a list like this is to go through the whole thing and rate each activity by interest and experience. Using a scale system, you can mark each option with the following (if you don't know what the activity is, check out the glossary, or search KinkAcademy.com or Google to find more information.)

NO   Zero interest/Hard Limit

1   Not very interesting, don't want to try it

2   Is up for discussion/Soft Limit

3   I could be interested in this if you are!

4   I'm very interested in doing this/Let's try it!

5   Favorite Activity/Top Pick

Or you can invent your own scale, but make sure you are clear about what each thing means!

Each profile page has additional space for you to elaborate on the following.

 GIVING / RECEIVING:
Do you like to give or receive this activity? Or both?

 GOAL FEELING(S):
How do you want to feel during the activity? Is that different than how you want to feel afterward?

 PREVIOUS EXPERIENCE:
Have you had any previous experience with this activity?

 LIMITATIONS:
Do you have any specific limitations around this activity?

 INTENSITY:
What level intensity do you enjoy this activity?
Low, Medium, High?

 RELATED INTERESTS:
Are there other activities or interests you like to enjoy at the same time as this activity, or before or after?

 ADDITIONAL THOUGHTS:
Do you have any additional thoughts about this activity that would be helpful to articulate? This can include specifics about the activity such as the types of tools used and your favorite positions.

The profiles are organized by category, but the energy you bring to an activity can change the experience of it dramatically, the way we discussed earlier in the Goal Feeling section.

There are also additional blank profile pages for you to add your own specific interests that may not have made it onto the list.

Are you unfamiliar with a term or activity? Check out KinkAcademy.com as a reliable, vetted resource for learning more.

Your body is a wonderland!

There are so many ways to use our bodies in erotic explorations: manipulating flesh, putting ourselves or our partners on display, the taboo of bodily fluids, and ways to be physical using nothing but your body. This kind of play can be primal and intimate, and it can be affected deeply by your own personal culture and relationship to your body.

Body image struggles are prevalent, so I'd recommend a positive approach unless a critical energy has been previously negotiated. There are as many ways to explore as there are bodies in the world.

BODY + BODILY FLUIDS

Armpit worship
Blood play
Body modification
Body paint
Body worship
Bukkake (cum on face)
Burping
Cum consumption
Endurance testing
Enemas
Exhibitionism
Farting
"Forced" nudity
"Forced" physical exercise
Golden Showers
    In mouth
    On body
Kicking
Lactation
Massage
Modeling for erotic photos
Menstruation
Nipple play
Nudity
Physical inspection
Pressure points
Rough body play
Scarification
Scat/Brown showers
Shaving
Showering together
Spit
Sweat
Take-down & capture
Voyeurism
Wrestling

GIVING / RECEIVING: INTEREST LEVEL: ◯

 GOAL FEELING(S):

BLOOD PLAY

 INTENSITY:

 LIMITATIONS:

 PREVIOUS EXPERIENCE:

 RELATED INTERESTS:

BLOOD PLAY

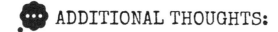 ADDITIONAL THOUGHTS:

 GIVING / RECEIVING: INTEREST LEVEL: ◯

 GOAL FEELING(S):

 INTENSITY:

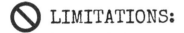 LIMITATIONS:

 PREVIOUS EXPERIENCE:

 RELATED INTERESTS:

EXHIBITIONISM

 ADDITIONAL THOUGHTS:

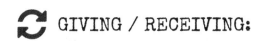 GIVING / RECEIVING: INTEREST LEVEL: ◯

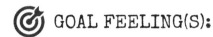 GOAL FEELING(S):

GOLDEN SHOWERS

 INTENSITY:

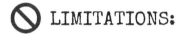 LIMITATIONS:

 PREVIOUS EXPERIENCE:

RELATED INTERESTS:

GOLDEN SHOWERS

 ADDITIONAL THOUGHTS:

GIVING / RECEIVING: INTEREST LEVEL: ◯

 GOAL FEELING(S):

MASSAGE

 INTENSITY:

◯ LIMITATIONS:

☑ PREVIOUS EXPERIENCE:

 RELATED INTERESTS:

MASSAGE

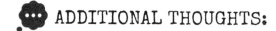 ADDITIONAL THOUGHTS:

GIVING / RECEIVING: INTEREST LEVEL: ◯

 GOAL FEELING(S):

NIPPLE PLAY

 INTENSITY:

 LIMITATIONS:

 PREVIOUS EXPERIENCE:

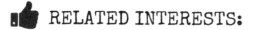 RELATED INTERESTS:

NIPPLE PLAY

 ADDITIONAL THOUGHTS:

GIVING / RECEIVING: INTEREST LEVEL: ◯

 GOAL FEELING(S):

 INTENSITY:

 LIMITATIONS:

 PREVIOUS EXPERIENCE:

PHYSICAL INSPECTION

65

 RELATED INTERESTS:

PHYSICAL INSPECTION

 ADDITIONAL THOUGHTS:

GIVING / RECEIVING:

INTEREST LEVEL: ◯

 GOAL FEELING(S):

ROUGH BODY PLAY

 INTENSITY:

 LIMITATIONS:

 PREVIOUS EXPERIENCE:

 RELATED INTERESTS:

ROUGH BODY PLAY

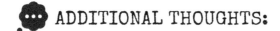 ADDITIONAL THOUGHTS:

GIVING / RECEIVING: INTEREST LEVEL: ◯

 GOAL FEELING(S):

 INTENSITY:

 LIMITATIONS:

🗹 PREVIOUS EXPERIENCE:

 RELATED INTERESTS:

VOYEURISM

 ADDITIONAL THOUGHTS:

Bondage, restraint, and sensory deprivation are classic elements of BDSM.

There are so many different ways to explore the feelings of restriction, different levels of encasement, and a huge variety of materials. For some, bondage can be like a loving hug, and for others an ever-tightening torment.

Special care must be taken for safety when you're incorporating bondage and sensory deprivation into your play. Make sure you have a safe gesture if speech will be restricted. Keep a pair of (quality) safety scissors close at hand. And never, NEVER leave a person in restrictive bondage completely alone and unmonitored.

BONDAGE + SENSORY DEPRIVATION

Blindfold

Bondage - arm/leg sleeves

Breast/chest bondage

Cage

Cock & ball bondage

Cock ring

Collar

Crotch tie

Gag

Ball gag

Funnel gag

Horse bit

O-ring gag

Gas mask

Genital bondage

Hair bondage

Handcuffs

Harness

Hogtie

Hood

Inflatables

Kinbaku

Leather cuffs + straps

Mental bondage

Mummification/encasement

Muzzle

Posture collar

Predicament situations

Self-suspension

Shibari

Sleep sack

Spreader bars

Stocks

Straitjacket

Suspension

Materials

Bondage tape

Chains

Coconut & sisal

Duct tape

Jute

Latex/rubber

Leather

Metal

Neckties

Nylon

Ribbons

Rope

Saran Wrap

GIVING / RECEIVING: INTEREST LEVEL:

GOAL FEELING(S):

INTENSITY:

LIMITATIONS:

PREVIOUS EXPERIENCE:

BLINDFOLD

 RELATED INTERESTS:

BLINDFOLD

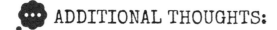 ADDITIONAL THOUGHTS:

GIVING / RECEIVING: INTEREST LEVEL:

GOAL FEELING(S):

INTENSITY:

LIMITATIONS:

GAG

PREVIOUS EXPERIENCE:

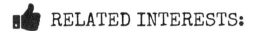 RELATED INTERESTS:

GAG

 ADDITIONAL THOUGHTS:

GIVING / RECEIVING:

INTEREST LEVEL: ◯

 GOAL FEELING(S):

INTENSITY:

LIMITATIONS:

HANDCUFFS

PREVIOUS EXPERIENCE:

 RELATED INTERESTS:

HANDCUFFS

 ADDITIONAL THOUGHTS:

GIVING / RECEIVING: INTEREST LEVEL: ◯

 GOAL FEELING(S):

INTENSITY:

⊘ LIMITATIONS:

HOOD

☑ PREVIOUS EXPERIENCE:

 RELATED INTERESTS:

HOOD

 ADDITIONAL THOUGHTS:

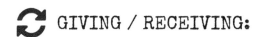 GIVING / RECEIVING: INTEREST LEVEL: ◯

 GOAL FEELING(S):

 INTENSITY:

🚫 LIMITATIONS:

📅 PREVIOUS EXPERIENCE:

 RELATED INTERESTS:

MUMMIFICATION / ENCASEMENT

 ADDITIONAL THOUGHTS:

GIVING / RECEIVING: INTEREST LEVEL: ◯

 GOAL FEELING(S):

 INTENSITY:

🚫 LIMITATIONS:

📋 PREVIOUS EXPERIENCE:

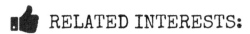 RELATED INTERESTS:

 PREDICAMENT SITUATIONS

 ADDITIONAL THOUGHTS:

GIVING / RECEIVING: INTEREST LEVEL: $\bigcirc$

 GOAL FEELING(S):

 INTENSITY:

🚫 LIMITATIONS:

📅 PREVIOUS EXPERIENCE:

 RELATED INTERESTS:

SUSPENSION

 ADDITIONAL THOUGHTS:

Clothes can serve so many purposes, from simple and functional to elaborate costumes.

For some, clothes are simply something to wear on their body. But for many, clothes go beyond fashion into self-expression. The clothing you wear can be deeply transformative, turning you into someone you want to be, or revealing your true self.

You might enjoy the rareness and classic fetish look of latex and leather. Or you might eroticize daily looks like sundresses, jeans, and sweaters. Corsets and catsuits are popular choices. No matter what you choose to wear (if you wear anything at all), the act of dressing up can be both fun and useful.

CLOTHES

1950's
Catsuit
Chainmail
Corporate/business
Corsets
Cross-dressing
Fishnets
"Forced" feminization
Fur (faux or real)
Gloves
Goth
Jeans
Kilts
Latex/rubber
Leather
Lingerie
PVC
Sissification
"Slutty" clothing
  In private
  In public
"Slutty" makeup
  In private
  In public
Spandex
Steampunk
Sundresses
Sweaters
Swimsuits
Uniforms
Vintage
Zentai

Other Material
  Lace
  Mesh
  Neoprene
  Satin
  Silk
  Suede

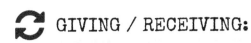 GIVING / RECEIVING: INTEREST LEVEL: ◯

GOAL FEELING(S):

INTENSITY:

LIMITATIONS:

PREVIOUS EXPERIENCE:

CROSS-DRESSING

 RELATED INTERESTS:

CROSS-DRESSING

 ADDITIONAL THOUGHTS:

GIVING / RECEIVING: INTEREST LEVEL: ◯

 GOAL FEELING(S):

LATEX / RUBBER

 INTENSITY:

🚫 **LIMITATIONS:**

📅 **PREVIOUS EXPERIENCE:**

👍 RELATED INTERESTS:

LATEX / RUBBER

💭 ADDITIONAL THOUGHTS:

92

↻ GIVING / RECEIVING:

INTEREST LEVEL: ◯

⊚ GOAL FEELING(S):

☼ INTENSITY:

⊘ LIMITATIONS:

☑ PREVIOUS EXPERIENCE:

LEATHER

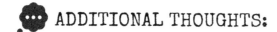 RELATED INTERESTS:

LEATHER

ADDITIONAL THOUGHTS:

GIVING / RECEIVING:

INTEREST LEVEL: ◯

GOAL FEELING(S):

INTENSITY:

LIMITATIONS:

PREVIOUS EXPERIENCE:

LINGERIE

 RELATED INTERESTS:

LINGERIE

 ADDITIONAL THOUGHTS:

GIVING / RECEIVING: INTEREST LEVEL: ◯

 GOAL FEELING(S):

 INTENSITY:

 LIMITATIONS:

☑ PREVIOUS EXPERIENCE:

UNIFORMS

 RELATED INTERESTS:

UNIFORMS

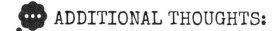 ADDITIONAL THOUGHTS:

There are many ways to be a foot lover, as an interest all its own or combined with other kinky fun.

Foot fetish is incredibly popular because there are just so many ways to enjoy our lowest extremities. Thanks to pop culture, it's one of the more mainstream known fetishes, though it's still presented in a pretty limited way.

Some foot lovers will enjoy anything to do with feet and others are more specific and singular in their tastes.

With all the different styles of shoes, stockings, socks, and jewelry, an ardent foot fan has a buffet of ways to accentuate their favorite pair of peds.

FOOT FETISH

Bare foot
    Clean feet
    Dirty/smelly feet
Bastinado
Boots
Cum on feet
Flip flops
Food smushing
Foot bondage
Foot job
Foot pampering
    Foot bath
    Massage
    Pedicure
Foot worship
High heels
Jewelry
    Ankle bracelet
    Toe rings
Nail polish
Socks
Stockings
    Thigh-high
    Pantyhose
    Garter belt
Sneakers
Tickling
Toe sucking
Trampling

GIVING / RECEIVING: INTEREST LEVEL: ◯

 GOAL FEELING(S):

 INTENSITY:

 LIMITATIONS:

BAREFOOT

PREVIOUS EXPERIENCE:

 RELATED INTERESTS:

BAREFOOT

 ADDITIONAL THOUGHTS:

GIVING / RECEIVING:

 GOAL FEELING(S):

 INTENSITY:

 LIMITATIONS:

BOOTS

 PREVIOUS EXPERIENCE:

 RELATED INTERESTS:

BOOTS

ADDITIONAL THOUGHTS:

C GIVING / RECEIVING:

INTEREST LEVEL: ◯

⊙ GOAL FEELING(S):

⏱ INTENSITY:

⊘ LIMITATIONS:

☑ PREVIOUS EXPERIENCE:

FOOT PAMPERING

 **RELATED INTERESTS:**

FOOT PAMPERING

 **ADDITIONAL THOUGHTS:**

GIVING / RECEIVING:

INTEREST LEVEL: ◯

GOAL FEELING(S):

INTENSITY:

LIMITATIONS:

PREVIOUS EXPERIENCE:

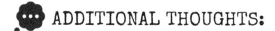
RELATED INTERESTS:

HIGH HEELS

ADDITIONAL THOUGHTS:

Erotic humiliation is a complex, varied, and mostly misunderstood kink.

Stereotypes and misconceptions can create apprehension about giving this intensely psychological kind of play a try, even for those who have a deep desire to experience it. The versatility of psychological torment is also impressive, and can be explored as anything from light-hearted teasing to deep degradation. It also makes a layered addition to other types of kinky play.

For those who find being human taxing (there are just so many things to manage!), dehumanization can be a welcome relief. By "removing humanity" to turn a kinkster into an inanimate object like art or furniture, they can experience a zen simplicity. Or by embodying an animal they can be released from the constraints of polite society.

HUMILIATION + DEHUMANIZATION

Being called "it" or "thing"
Blackmail & "being outed"
Body-image insults
Corner time
Cuckolding
    Cuckqueening
Dehumanization
Diapers
Dollification
Gender-based insults
Human furniture
Intelligence-based insults
Mouth-soaping
Predicament situations
Public humiliation
    General world
    Kink events
Sexual objectification
Small penis humiliation (sph)
Verbal degradation
Wearing demeaning signs
Writing on body

GIVING / RECEIVING: INTEREST LEVEL:

 GOAL FEELING(S):

 INTENSITY:

 LIMITATIONS:

CUCKOLDING

 PREVIOUS EXPERIENCE:

 RELATED INTERESTS:

CUCKOLDING

 ADDITIONAL THOUGHTS:

🔄 GIVING / RECEIVING: INTEREST LEVEL: ◯

🎯 GOAL FEELING(S):

 INTENSITY:

🚫 LIMITATIONS:

HUMAN FURNITURE

🗓️ PREVIOUS EXPERIENCE:

 RELATED INTERESTS:

HUMAN FURNITURE

 ADDITIONAL THOUGHTS:

GIVING / RECEIVING: INTEREST LEVEL: ◯

GOAL FEELING(S):

INTENSITY:

LIMITATIONS:

PUBLIC HUMILIATION

PREVIOUS EXPERIENCE:

 RELATED INTERESTS:

PUBLIC HUMILIATION

 ADDITIONAL THOUGHTS:

GIVING / RECEIVING: INTEREST LEVEL: ◯

 GOAL FEELING(S):

 INTENSITY:

LIMITATIONS:

SEXUAL OBJECTIFICATION

PREVIOUS EXPERIENCE:

 RELATED INTERESTS:

SEXUAL OBJECTIFICATION

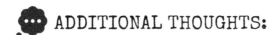 ADDITIONAL THOUGHTS:

From soft and sensual to sharp and sadistic, there are many ways to incorporate sensation into a sexy scene.

People love to explore sensation, whether it is the caress of bunny fur or the snap of a sharp whip. So many of the things we do are centered in creating a distinct, unusual, or intense sensation as a path to physical and mental pleasure.

You can accumulate a heavy toy bag, full of toys that are expensive and embellished and made by community craftspeople. Or you can use anything handy (including your hands!) or DIY toys with easy-to-find elements to keep your sexual adventures casual and spontaneous.

IMPACT + SENSATION

Bastinado
Biting
Branding
Bunny fur
Caning
Clamps + clips
Clothespins
Corporal punishment
Cutting
Electricity
 E-stim
 TENS unit
 Violet wand
Face slapping
Figging
Fire cupping
Fire play
Flogging
Genital torment
Hair pulling
Needle play
Nipple torment
Over-the-knee spanking
Piercing
Pinching
Punching
Scratching
Soft touch
Spanking
Temperature play
Urethral sounds
Wax
Whipping

Bruising
 Heavy
 Light

Marks
 Heavy
 Light

Pain
 Heavy
 Light

Sensual
Sadistic

Tools
 Belt
 Cane
 Dragontail
 Hairbrush
 Hand
 Paddle - acrylic
 Paddle - leather
 Paddle - wooden
 Riding crop
 Singletail
 Wartenberg pinwheels

🔄 GIVING / RECEIVING: INTEREST LEVEL: ◯

🎯 GOAL FEELING(S):

🌡️ INTENSITY:

🚫 LIMITATIONS:

BITING

☑️ PREVIOUS EXPERIENCE:

 **RELATED INTERESTS:**

BITING

 **ADDITIONAL THOUGHTS:**

GIVING / RECEIVING: INTEREST LEVEL:

 GOAL FEELING(S):

 INTENSITY:

 LIMITATIONS:

CANING

☑ PREVIOUS EXPERIENCE:

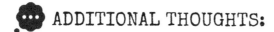 RELATED INTERESTS:

CANING

ADDITIONAL THOUGHTS:

🔄 GIVING / RECEIVING: INTEREST LEVEL: ◯

🎯 GOAL FEELING(S):

🌡️ INTENSITY:

🚫 LIMITATIONS:

CLAMPS + CLIPS

☑️ PREVIOUS EXPERIENCE:

 RELATED INTERESTS:

CLAMPS + CLIPS

ADDITIONAL THOUGHTS:

GIVING / RECEIVING:

 GOAL FEELING(S):

 INTENSITY:

 LIMITATIONS:

ELECTRICITY

PREVIOUS EXPERIENCE:

 RELATED INTERESTS:

ELECTRICITY

 ADDITIONAL THOUGHTS:

 **GIVING / RECEIVING:**

GOAL FEELING(S):

INTENSITY:

LIMITATIONS:

 **PREVIOUS EXPERIENCE:**

FLOGGING

 RELATED INTERESTS:

FLOGGING

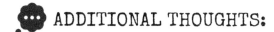 ADDITIONAL THOUGHTS:

GIVING / RECEIVING:

GOAL FEELING(S):

INTENSITY:

LIMITATIONS:

GENITAL TORMENT

PREVIOUS EXPERIENCE:

 RELATED INTERESTS:

GENITAL TORMENT

 ADDITIONAL THOUGHTS:

GIVING / RECEIVING:

INTEREST LEVEL: ◯

GOAL FEELING(S):

 INTENSITY:

🚫 **LIMITATIONS:**

☑ **PREVIOUS EXPERIENCE:**

 RELATED INTERESTS:

HAIR PULLING

 ADDITIONAL THOUGHTS:

🔄 GIVING / RECEIVING: INTEREST LEVEL: ◯

🎯 GOAL FEELING(S):

🌡️ INTENSITY:

🚫 LIMITATIONS:

SPANKING

✅ PREVIOUS EXPERIENCE:

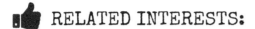 RELATED INTERESTS:

SPANKING

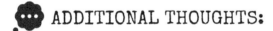 ADDITIONAL THOUGHTS:

GIVING / RECEIVING:

GOAL FEELING(S):

INTENSITY:

LIMITATIONS:

TEMPERATURE PLAY

 PREVIOUS EXPERIENCE:

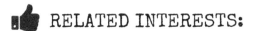 **RELATED INTERESTS:**

 **ADDITIONAL THOUGHTS:**

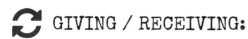 GIVING / RECEIVING: INTEREST LEVEL:

 GOAL FEELING(S):

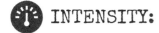 INTENSITY:

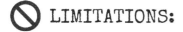 LIMITATIONS:

WAX PLAY

 PREVIOUS EXPERIENCE:

 RELATED INTERESTS:

WAX PLAY

 ADDITIONAL THOUGHTS:

 GIVING / RECEIVING: INTEREST LEVEL:

GOAL FEELING(S):

INTENSITY:

LIMITATIONS:

 WHIPPING

PREVIOUS EXPERIENCE:

 RELATED INTERESTS:

WHIPPING

 ADDITIONAL THOUGHTS:

Many of the activities in this book would fit into other categories, and some don't fit into any at all.

This catch-all section is for interests that didn't easily fit into the other categories listed. Activities can change depending on the energy and specifics of the scene.

Many actions can be combined or used in a series to create a sexual or kinky scene that is highly personalized. They are building blocks to creating your desired headspace, so mix and match to your heart (and body's) content!

MISCELLANEOUS

Abandonment

ABDL - Adult Baby, Diaper Lover

Balloons (Looners)

Breath play

   Choking

   Hand over face

   Pillow over face

Cigar play

   Ashtray service

   Cigar service

   Swallowing ash

Crying

Energy play

Ethical non-monogamy

Fear play

Feederism

Figging

Financial domination

Flesh hooks

Food play (sploshing)

Furry

Gender-bending

Hentai

HuCow (human cow)

Knife play

Mind fuck

Monogamy

Polyamory

Race play

Tattoos

Transformation

   Growing (Giantess)

   Shrinking

Tickling

Watching pornography

Waterboarding

MISCELLANEOUS

🔁 GIVING / RECEIVING: INTEREST LEVEL: ◯

🎯 GOAL FEELING(S):

🌡 INTENSITY:

🚫 LIMITATIONS:

☑ PREVIOUS EXPERIENCE:

 RELATED INTERESTS:

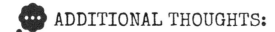 ADDITIONAL THOUGHTS:

GIVING / RECEIVING: INTEREST LEVEL: 〇

 GOAL FEELING(S):

 INTENSITY:

 LIMITATIONS:

CIGAR PLAY

📅 PREVIOUS EXPERIENCE:

147

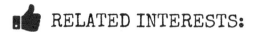 RELATED INTERESTS:

 ADDITIONAL THOUGHTS:

GIVING / RECEIVING: INTEREST LEVEL: ◯

 GOAL FEELING(S):

 INTENSITY:

 LIMITATIONS:

CRYING

 PREVIOUS EXPERIENCE:

RELATED INTERESTS:

CRYING

 ADDITIONAL THOUGHTS:

GIVING / RECEIVING:

 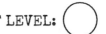

 GOAL FEELING(S):

 INTENSITY:

 LIMITATIONS:

ENERGY PLAY

 PREVIOUS EXPERIENCE:

👍 RELATED INTERESTS:

ENERGY PLAY

💭 ADDITIONAL THOUGHTS:

🔄 GIVING / RECEIVING: INTEREST LEVEL: ◯

🎯 GOAL FEELING(S):

🌡 INTENSITY:

🚫 LIMITATIONS:

FEAR PLAY

✅ PREVIOUS EXPERIENCE:

 RELATED INTERESTS:

 ADDITIONAL THOUGHTS:

⟳ GIVING / RECEIVING: INTEREST LEVEL: ◯

◎ GOAL FEELING(S):

🌡 INTENSITY:

🚫 LIMITATIONS:

FOOD PLAY

☑ PREVIOUS EXPERIENCE:

 RELATED INTERESTS:

FOOD PLAY

 ADDITIONAL THOUGHTS:

GIVING / RECEIVING:

INTEREST LEVEL:

GOAL FEELING(S):

INTENSITY:

LIMITATIONS:

TICKLING

PREVIOUS EXPERIENCE:

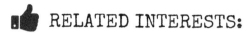 RELATED INTERESTS:

TICKLING

 ADDITIONAL THOUGHTS:

Choosing to give up or take control can be intensely powerful, and protocols can give everyday actions more meaning.

Power exchange is another classic element of kink exploration, but this is a good place to remind you that you don't have to be into dominance and submission in order to enjoy other aspects of creative sexuality. But if you do enjoy power exchange, then it can heighten every other activity you do.

Contrary to popular belief, very few people are ALL dominant, or ALL submissive. Like everything else, those desires can exist on a spectrum. You might innately feel drawn to one side of the power dynamic or another, or it might depend on who you're playing with or what you're doing, or even where you are in your kink journey.

Protocols are a way of defining exactly how something is to be done. From personal restrictions and customs to connection-building rituals, there are many ways you can use protocols for pleasure or practicality.

POWER EXCHANGE + PROTOCOL

Bathroom restrictions
Being "all-powerful"
Being "loaned out" for service
Being "powerless"
Bootblack
Brat play
CFNM - Clothed Female Naked Male
Consensual non-consent
Crawling
Denial of speaking
Discipline + punishment
Domestic chores
Dominance
Eye-contact restrictions
Gorean
Kneeling
Leash training
Master/slave
Obedience training
Ownership (owning/being owned)
Protocol training - submissive positions
Service relationship
Serving as a maid or butler
Submission
Switching
Time-out punishment
Wearing leash & collar

GIVING / RECEIVING: INTEREST LEVEL: ◯

 GOAL FEELING(S):

 INTENSITY:

 LIMITATIONS:

 PREVIOUS EXPERIENCE:

CONSENSUAL NON-CONSENT

 RELATED INTERESTS:

 ADDITIONAL THOUGHTS:

🔁 GIVING / RECEIVING: INTEREST LEVEL: ◯

🎯 GOAL FEELING(S):

🌡️ INTENSITY:

🚫 LIMITATIONS:

📅 PREVIOUS EXPERIENCE:

DISCIPLINE + PUNISHMENT

 RELATED INTERESTS:

DISCIPLINE + PUNISHMENT

 ADDITIONAL THOUGHTS:

🔄 GIVING / RECEIVING:

INTEREST LEVEL: ◯

🎯 GOAL FEELING(S):

🌡 INTENSITY:

🚫 LIMITATIONS:

☑ PREVIOUS EXPERIENCE:

 RELATED INTERESTS:

DOMESTIC CHORES

 ADDITIONAL THOUGHTS:

🔄 GIVING / RECEIVING: INTEREST LEVEL: ◯

🎯 GOAL FEELING(S):

🌡 INTENSITY:

🚫 LIMITATIONS:

DOMINANCE

🗓 PREVIOUS EXPERIENCE:

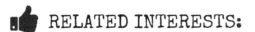 RELATED INTERESTS:

DOMINANCE

 ADDITIONAL THOUGHTS:

🔄 GIVING / RECEIVING: INTEREST LEVEL: ◯

🎯 GOAL FEELING(S):

🌡 INTENSITY:

🚫 LIMITATIONS:

KNEELING

📅 PREVIOUS EXPERIENCE:

169

 RELATED INTERESTS:

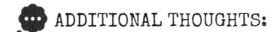 ADDITIONAL THOUGHTS:

KNEELING

GIVING / RECEIVING: INTEREST LEVEL:

GOAL FEELING(S):

INTENSITY:

LIMITATIONS:

PREVIOUS EXPERIENCE:

LEASH + COLLAR

171

 RELATED INTERESTS:

LEASH + COLLAR

 ADDITIONAL THOUGHTS:

🔄 GIVING / RECEIVING: INTEREST LEVEL: ⃝

⌖ GOAL FEELING(S):

🌡 INTENSITY:

🚫 LIMITATIONS:

 PREVIOUS EXPERIENCE:

 RELATED INTERESTS:

SERVICE RELATIONSHIP

 ADDITIONAL THOUGHTS:

C GIVING / RECEIVING: INTEREST LEVEL:

G GOAL FEELING(S):

T INTENSITY:

O LIMITATIONS:

SUBMISSION

☑ PREVIOUS EXPERIENCE:

 RELATED INTERESTS:

 ADDITIONAL THOUGHTS:

GIVING / RECEIVING:

INTEREST LEVEL: ◯

GOAL FEELING(S):

INTENSITY:

LIMITATIONS:

PREVIOUS EXPERIENCE:

SWITCHING

177

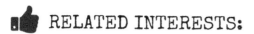 RELATED INTERESTS:

 ADDITIONAL THOUGHTS:

SWITCHING

Use the power of your imagination to explore other characters and scenarios.

Role-play can be a fantasy role that you playfully take on for a short period of time, or it can refer to a role that you take more seriously and forms a central part of your kink identity. Role-play can be a way that you can break out of a rut or spice up your creativity, and can give you a natural plot to follow and dialogue to work with.

Remember, you're not trying to win any awards! Don't take yourself too seriously and be willing to have fun and allow for imperfection. You'll have more success if you really get into it, rather than try to play it cool and treat it as nonsense.

Get in touch with your inner sense of fantasy and suspend your disbelief. Use props and clothing bits and pieces to bring your inspiration to life.

ROLE-PLAY

Age play
Aliens
Animals
   Kitten play
   Pig
   Pony play
      Donkey
      Show pony
      Work horse
   Puppy play
      Collar training
      Grooming
      Tricks
Art/statue
Cheerleader/jock
Clowns
Damsel-in-distress
DDlg - Daddy Dom, little girl
Escort/stripper/customer
Fantasy gang rape
Incest
Interrogation
Kidnapping
Medical
Military
Prison
Ravishment
Religious
School
Superheroes
Supernatural
   Demon
   Vampire
   Werewolf
   Witch/wizard
Virgin/innocent

ROLE-PLAY

GIVING / RECEIVING: INTEREST LEVEL:

GOAL FEELING(S):

INTENSITY:

LIMITATIONS:

PREVIOUS EXPERIENCE:

 RELATED INTERESTS:

 ADDITIONAL THOUGHTS:

AGE PLAY

GIVING / RECEIVING: INTEREST LEVEL: ◯

 GOAL FEELING(S):

 INTENSITY:

 LIMITATIONS:

INTERROGATION

 PREVIOUS EXPERIENCE:

 RELATED INTERESTS:

 ADDITIONAL THOUGHTS:

🔁 GIVING / RECEIVING: INTEREST LEVEL: ◯

🎯 GOAL FEELING(S):

🌡 INTENSITY:

🚫 LIMITATIONS:

MEDICAL

☑ PREVIOUS EXPERIENCE:

RELATED INTERESTS:

ADDITIONAL THOUGHTS:

MEDICAL

🔁 GIVING / RECEIVING: INTEREST LEVEL:

🎯 GOAL FEELING(S):

🌡️ INTENSITY:

🚫 LIMITATIONS:

PRISON

📅 PREVIOUS EXPERIENCE:

187

 RELATED INTERESTS:

 ADDITIONAL THOUGHTS:

PRISON

🔄 GIVING / RECEIVING: INTEREST LEVEL: ◯

🎯 GOAL FEELING(S):

🌡 INTENSITY:

🚫 LIMITATIONS:

🗓 PREVIOUS EXPERIENCE:

 RELATED INTERESTS:

RAVISHMENT

 ADDITIONAL THOUGHTS:

🔄 GIVING / RECEIVING:

INTEREST LEVEL: ◯

🎯 GOAL FEELING(S):

🌡 INTENSITY:

🚫 LIMITATIONS:

📅 PREVIOUS EXPERIENCE:

SCHOOL

191

 RELATED INTERESTS:

 ADDITIONAL THOUGHTS:

SCHOOL

Erotic adventures can be conventional or exotic, but the most important thing is that they're satisfying.

When it comes to creative sexuality, it's pretty amazing that the things that arouse us go far beyond what's in our pants. But then again, what's in our pants can be a source of great pleasure, too.

Alone, with a partner, or with a group, we can bring our most arousing desires to life, or keep them as favorite fantasies. Sex toys are made in a selection of materials including metal, glass, and silicone, and can be used to enhance your erotic experiences.

SEX + ORGASM CONTROL

Anal
Being "caught" masturbating
Being "loaned out" for sex
Chastity
  Orgasm denial
  Devices
Cock worship
Deep-throating
Double penetration
Edging
Face-fucking
Fingerbanging
Fisting
  Anal
  Vaginal
Forced orgasm
"Forced" bisexuality
"Forced" to suck a strap-on
Fucking machines
Group sex
  Threesomes
  Orgies
Hand-jobs (giving/receiving)
Kissing
Licking
Masturbation instruction
Mutual masturbation
Mutual oral sex ("69")
Oral sex
Outdoor sex
Pegging
Prostate massage
Pussy worship
Rimming
Rough sex
Ruined orgasm

Sex in public
Sex toys
  Butt plug
  Dildo
  Strap-on dildo
  Vibrator
Sex Toy Materials
  Silicone
  Glass
  Metal
Sex with strangers
Squirting
Swinging
Tantra
Tease + denial
Triple penetration
Queening

GIVING / RECEIVING: 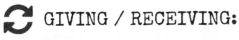 INTEREST LEVEL:

 GOAL FEELING(S):

 INTENSITY:

 LIMITATIONS:

ANAL

 PREVIOUS EXPERIENCE:

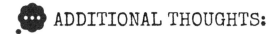

👍 RELATED INTERESTS:

💭 ADDITIONAL THOUGHTS:

ANAL

GIVING / RECEIVING:

 GOAL FEELING(S):

 INTENSITY:

 LIMITATIONS:

CHASTITY

 PREVIOUS EXPERIENCE:

 RELATED INTERESTS:

 ADDITIONAL THOUGHTS:

CHASTITY

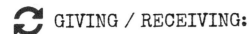 GIVING / RECEIVING: INTEREST LEVEL: ◯

🎯 GOAL FEELING(S):

🌡 INTENSITY:

🚫 LIMITATIONS:

📅 PREVIOUS EXPERIENCE:

FISTING

 RELATED INTERESTS:

 ADDITIONAL THOUGHTS:

FISTING

GIVING / RECEIVING:　INTEREST LEVEL: ◯

GOAL FEELING(S):

 INTENSITY:

LIMITATIONS:

PREVIOUS EXPERIENCE:

 RELATED INTERESTS:

 ADDITIONAL THOUGHTS:

GROUP SEX

GIVING / RECEIVING: INTEREST LEVEL: ◯

🎯 GOAL FEELING(S):

🎛 INTENSITY:

🚫 LIMITATIONS:

📅 PREVIOUS EXPERIENCE:

 RELATED INTERESTS:

 ADDITIONAL THOUGHTS:

MASTURBATION INSTRUCTION

GIVING / RECEIVING: INTEREST LEVEL: ◯

GOAL FEELING(S):

INTENSITY:

LIMITATIONS:

PREVIOUS EXPERIENCE:

MUTUAL MASTURBATION

205

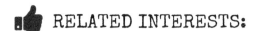 RELATED INTERESTS:

 ADDITIONAL THOUGHTS:

MUTUAL MASTURBATION

GIVING / RECEIVING: INTEREST LEVEL: ◯

 GOAL FEELING(S):

 INTENSITY:

 LIMITATIONS:

ORAL SEX

 PREVIOUS EXPERIENCE:

 RELATED INTERESTS:

 ADDITIONAL THOUGHTS:

ORAL SEX

GIVING / RECEIVING: INTEREST LEVEL:

GOAL FEELING(S):

INTENSITY:

LIMITATIONS:

PREVIOUS EXPERIENCE:

ROUGH SEX

 RELATED INTERESTS:

 ADDITIONAL THOUGHTS:

ROUGH SEX

GIVING / RECEIVING:

INTEREST LEVEL: ◯

 GOAL FEELING(S):

 INTENSITY:

 LIMITATIONS:

SEX TOYS

 PREVIOUS EXPERIENCE:

 RELATED INTERESTS:

 ADDITIONAL THOUGHTS:

SEX TOYS

🔄 GIVING / RECEIVING:

INTEREST LEVEL: ◯

🎯 GOAL FEELING(S):

🌡 INTENSITY:

🚫 LIMITATIONS:

✅ PREVIOUS EXPERIENCE:

SWINGING

213

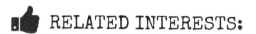 RELATED INTERESTS:

 ADDITIONAL THOUGHTS:

SWINGING

 GIVING / RECEIVING:

INTEREST LEVEL: ◯

 GOAL FEELING(S):

INTENSITY:

LIMITATIONS:

PREVIOUS EXPERIENCE:

TEASE + DENIAL

 RELATED INTERESTS:

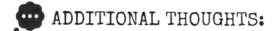 ADDITIONAL THOUGHTS:

TEASE + DENIAL

Words can evoke your desired headspace and can heighten any experience, if you'll let your mouth run away with you.

Regardless of what's happening to our body, words bring awareness to our most powerful sexual organ, our mind. Since we're typically discouraged from using "vulgar" language in our everyday life, saying or hearing sexually taboo words can be invigorating in a very special way.

Practice saying words that turn you on when you're enjoying private time alone, and you'll find yourself masturbating to new heights of pleasure, all while getting more comfortable talking dirty. Vary your tone of voice and the way you deliver a line to make your words more impactful to yourself and your partner.

VERBAL + VOCABULARY LIST

Begging

Confession - fantasies, etc

Hypnosis

Mantras

Phone sex

Quizzes & tests

Reading erotica

Scolding

Self-humbling

Talking dirty

Writing sentences

Vocabulary list

GIVING / RECEIVING: INTEREST LEVEL:

 GOAL FEELING(S):

 INTENSITY:

 LIMITATIONS:

PREVIOUS EXPERIENCE:

BEGGING

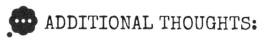 RELATED INTERESTS:

👍 ADDITIONAL THOUGHTS:

BEGGING

GIVING / RECEIVING: INTEREST LEVEL:

GOAL FEELING(S):

INTENSITY:

LIMITATIONS:

PREVIOUS EXPERIENCE:

CONFESSION

221

 RELATED INTERESTS:

 ADDITIONAL THOUGHTS:

CONFESSION

GIVING / RECEIVING: INTEREST LEVEL:

 GOAL FEELING(S):

 INTENSITY:

 LIMITATIONS:

 PREVIOUS EXPERIENCE:

HYPNOSIS

 RELATED INTERESTS:

 ADDITIONAL THOUGHTS:

HYPNOSIS

🔄 GIVING / RECEIVING:

INTEREST LEVEL: ◯

🎯 GOAL FEELING(S):

🌡️ INTENSITY:

🚫 LIMITATIONS:

☑️ PREVIOUS EXPERIENCE:

TALKING DIRTY

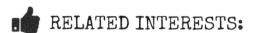 RELATED INTERESTS:

 ADDITIONAL THOUGHTS:

TALKING DIRTY

ashtray

ass

baby

beg

bitch

breasts

butthole

cock

come for me

court jester

crave

creamy

cuckold

cum

cunt

cunt juice

deep throat

deeper

degraded

desperate

dick

dirty

disgusting

dog

dripping

embarrassed

face-fuck

fairy

filthy

flesh

force

freak

fuck

fuck doll

fuck me

garbage

good boy/good girl

hard-on

harder

hole

horny

hot

humiliated

insatiable

insect

insignificant

jack off

jizz

juicy

kneel

knockers

lewd

lick

lover

lowly

lustful

lusty

meat

mine

nasty

naughty

now

nutsack

pansy

pathetic

pervert

piece of ass

pig

please

pleasure
prick
pussy
randy
ravage
ravish
satisfy
scum
sexy
sinful
sissy
skank
slave
sleazy
slit
sloppy
slower
slut
slut-buttons
smack
smart ass
splunk
squirm
squirt
stud
subbie
suck
tease
thing
thrust
tight ass
tits
Toilet
trash
twat

used
vixen
vulgar
wanker
want
weenie
wet
whore
wild thing
wimpy
yes

Add Your Own

Our sexual needs are a unique and personal matrix of desires, both hidden and known.

This section is full of blank profiles, so you can look at the full activity lists that start each category and devote a full page to any of the additional interests you enjoy.

Use your pen to write the activity or interest on the grey tab at the edge of the page. Then fill out the profile like usual!

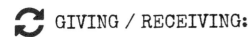 GIVING / RECEIVING: 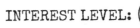INTEREST LEVEL:

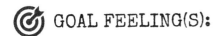 GOAL FEELING(S):

INTENSITY:

LIMITATIONS:

PREVIOUS EXPERIENCE:

 RELATED INTERESTS:

💭 ADDITIONAL THOUGHTS:

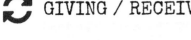 GIVING / RECEIVING: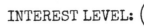

 GOAL FEELING(S):

 INTENSITY:

LIMITATIONS:

 PREVIOUS EXPERIENCE:

233

 RELATED INTERESTS:

 ADDITIONAL THOUGHTS:

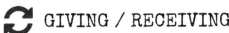 GIVING / RECEIVING:  INTEREST LEVEL: ◯

 GOAL FEELING(S):

🌡️ INTENSITY:

🚫 LIMITATIONS:

 PREVIOUS EXPERIENCE:

235

 RELATED INTERESTS:

 ADDITIONAL THOUGHTS:

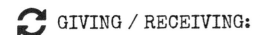 GIVING / RECEIVING: 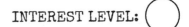 INTEREST LEVEL: ◯

GOAL FEELING(S):

INTENSITY:

LIMITATIONS:

PREVIOUS EXPERIENCE:

 RELATED INTERESTS:

 ADDITIONAL THOUGHTS:

 GIVING / RECEIVING: 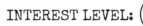 INTEREST LEVEL: ◯

 GOAL FEELING(S):

🌡 INTENSITY:

🚫 LIMITATIONS:

☑ PREVIOUS EXPERIENCE:

 RELATED INTERESTS:

 ADDITIONAL THOUGHTS:

 GIVING / RECEIVING: 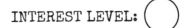 INTEREST LEVEL:

GOAL FEELING(S):

INTENSITY:

LIMITATIONS:

PREVIOUS EXPERIENCE:

 RELATED INTERESTS:

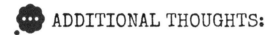 ADDITIONAL THOUGHTS:

 GIVING / RECEIVING: 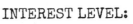 INTEREST LEVEL:

 GOAL FEELING(S):

INTENSITY:

LIMITATIONS:

 PREVIOUS EXPERIENCE:

 RELATED INTERESTS:

ADDITIONAL THOUGHTS:

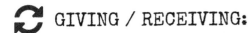 GIVING / RECEIVING: 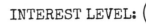 INTEREST LEVEL:

 GOAL FEELING(S):

 INTENSITY:

 LIMITATIONS:

 PREVIOUS EXPERIENCE:

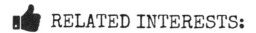 RELATED INTERESTS:

ADDITIONAL THOUGHTS:

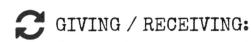 GIVING / RECEIVING: 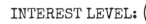 INTEREST LEVEL:

 GOAL FEELING(S):

INTENSITY:

LIMITATIONS:

 PREVIOUS EXPERIENCE:

 **RELATED INTERESTS:**

ADDITIONAL THOUGHTS:

 GIVING / RECEIVING: 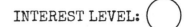 INTEREST LEVEL:

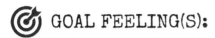 GOAL FEELING(S):

INTENSITY:

LIMITATIONS:

PREVIOUS EXPERIENCE:

 RELATED INTERESTS:

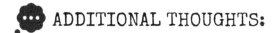 ADDITIONAL THOUGHTS:

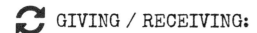 GIVING / RECEIVING: 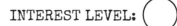 INTEREST LEVEL:

GOAL FEELING(S):

INTENSITY:

LIMITATIONS:

PREVIOUS EXPERIENCE:

 RELATED INTERESTS:

 ADDITIONAL THOUGHTS:

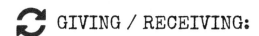 **GIVING / RECEIVING:** 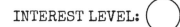 INTEREST LEVEL:

 **GOAL FEELING(S):**

INTENSITY:

LIMITATIONS:

PREVIOUS EXPERIENCE:

253

 RELATED INTERESTS:

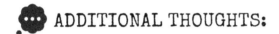 ADDITIONAL THOUGHTS:

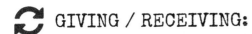 GIVING / RECEIVING:

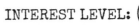 INTEREST LEVEL:

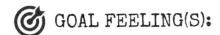 GOAL FEELING(S):

INTENSITY:

LIMITATIONS:

PREVIOUS EXPERIENCE:

 **RELATED INTERESTS:**

ADDITIONAL THOUGHTS:

GIVING / RECEIVING: 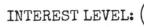INTEREST LEVEL: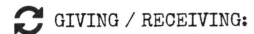

 GOAL FEELING(S):

 INTENSITY:

 LIMITATIONS:

 PREVIOUS EXPERIENCE:

 RELATED INTERESTS:

 ADDITIONAL THOUGHTS:

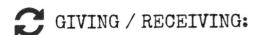 GIVING / RECEIVING: INTEREST LEVEL:

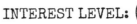 GOAL FEELING(S):

 INTENSITY:

 LIMITATIONS:

 PREVIOUS EXPERIENCE:

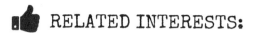 RELATED INTERESTS:

 ADDITIONAL THOUGHTS:

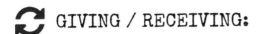 GIVING / RECEIVING:

INTEREST LEVEL: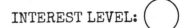

GOAL FEELING(S):

INTENSITY:

LIMITATIONS:

PREVIOUS EXPERIENCE:

261

 RELATED INTERESTS:

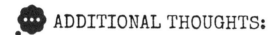 ADDITIONAL THOUGHTS:

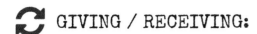 GIVING / RECEIVING: 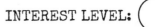 INTEREST LEVEL: ◯

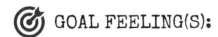 GOAL FEELING(S):

🌡 INTENSITY:

🚫 LIMITATIONS:

✅ PREVIOUS EXPERIENCE:

 RELATED INTERESTS:

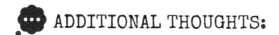 ADDITIONAL THOUGHTS:

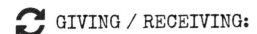 **GIVING / RECEIVING:**  INTEREST LEVEL:

 **GOAL FEELING(S):**

INTENSITY:

LIMITATIONS:

PREVIOUS EXPERIENCE:

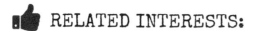 RELATED INTERESTS:

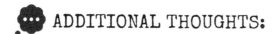 ADDITIONAL THOUGHTS:

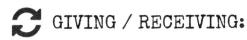 **GIVING / RECEIVING:**  INTEREST LEVEL: ◯

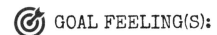 **GOAL FEELING(S):**

INTENSITY:

LIMITATIONS:

PREVIOUS EXPERIENCE:

 RELATED INTERESTS:

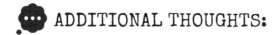 ADDITIONAL THOUGHTS:

GIVING / RECEIVING: 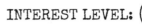 INTEREST LEVEL:

 GOAL FEELING(S):

 INTENSITY:

 LIMITATIONS:

 PREVIOUS EXPERIENCE:

 **RELATED INTERESTS:**

ADDITIONAL THOUGHTS:

GIVING / RECEIVING: 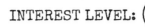INTEREST LEVEL:

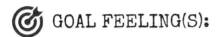 GOAL FEELING(S):

 INTENSITY:

 LIMITATIONS:

 PREVIOUS EXPERIENCE:

271

 RELATED INTERESTS:

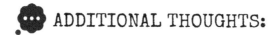 ADDITIONAL THOUGHTS:

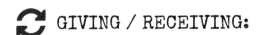 GIVING / RECEIVING: INTEREST LEVEL: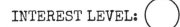

 GOAL FEELING(S):

INTENSITY:

LIMITATIONS:

PREVIOUS EXPERIENCE:

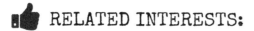 RELATED INTERESTS:

 ADDITIONAL THOUGHTS:

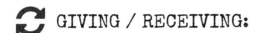 GIVING / RECEIVING: 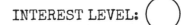 INTEREST LEVEL: ◯

GOAL FEELING(S):

INTENSITY:

LIMITATIONS:

PREVIOUS EXPERIENCE:

275

 RELATED INTERESTS:

💭 ADDITIONAL THOUGHTS:

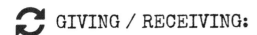 GIVING / RECEIVING:

 GOAL FEELING(S):

INTENSITY:

LIMITATIONS:

 PREVIOUS EXPERIENCE:

 RELATED INTERESTS:

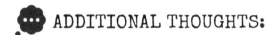 ADDITIONAL THOUGHTS:

GIVING / RECEIVING: 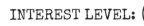 INTEREST LEVEL:

 GOAL FEELING(S):

 INTENSITY:

 LIMITATIONS:

 PREVIOUS EXPERIENCE:

 RELATED INTERESTS:

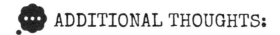 ADDITIONAL THOUGHTS:

GIVING / RECEIVING:  INTEREST LEVEL:

 GOAL FEELING(S):

 INTENSITY:

 LIMITATIONS:

 PREVIOUS EXPERIENCE:

 RELATED INTERESTS:

 ADDITIONAL THOUGHTS:

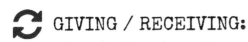 **GIVING / RECEIVING:** **INTEREST LEVEL:**

GOAL FEELING(S):

INTENSITY:

LIMITATIONS:

PREVIOUS EXPERIENCE:

283

 RELATED INTERESTS:

ADDITIONAL THOUGHTS:

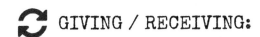 GIVING / RECEIVING: INTEREST LEVEL:

 GOAL FEELING(S):

🎯 INTENSITY:

🚫 LIMITATIONS:

✅ PREVIOUS EXPERIENCE:

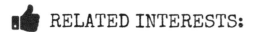 RELATED INTERESTS:

 ADDITIONAL THOUGHTS:

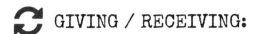 GIVING / RECEIVING:  INTEREST LEVEL: ◯

 GOAL FEELING(S):

🕐 INTENSITY:

🚫 LIMITATIONS:

☑ PREVIOUS EXPERIENCE:

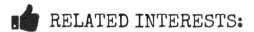 RELATED INTERESTS:

 ADDITIONAL THOUGHTS:

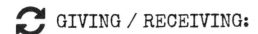 GIVING / RECEIVING:  INTEREST LEVEL:

 GOAL FEELING(S):

INTENSITY:

LIMITATIONS:

PREVIOUS EXPERIENCE:

 **RELATED INTERESTS:**

 **ADDITIONAL THOUGHTS:**

NOTES

NOTES

NOTES

NOTES

NOTES

NOTES

NOTES

Check out

YesNoMaybeWorkbook.com

for related products and
additional resources.

Ready, Kink, Go! – Negotiation Deck
Kink Talk – Discussion Prompts
365 Days of Kink – Journal

MEET THE AUTHOR

Princess Kali is the founder of Kink
Academy, a life-long entrepreneur,
and a relentless creator.

She's also the author of:
- Enough to Make You Blush:
  Exploring Erotic Humiliation
- Authentic Kink
- 365 Days of Kink Journal

Kali's greatest joy is teaching kink
classes and helping kinksters and all
sexual adventurers have safer, more
satisfying, creative and joyful
experiences.

KINK
ACADEMY

You've grown up,
and so should your sex education.

Kink Academy is a comprehensive library of sex-ed videos for adventurous, consenting adults. Whether you're new to kink or an experienced player, there's something for everyone to learn on Kink Academy.

With over 2,000 sex-ed videos and over 150 sexuality educators, the Kink Academy Team works with sex, kink, gender, and relationship experts from around the world to present the most diverse and experienced voices possible for your ongoing sexual education.

KinkAcademy.com

Made in the USA
Columbia, SC
05 February 2024

31449718R00167